BATWOMAN
elegy

GREG RUCKA WRITER

J.H WILLIAMS III ARTIST

DAVE STEWART COLORIST

TODD KLEIN LETTERS

BATMAN CREATED BY BOB KANE

MICHAEL SIGLAIN EDITOR-ORIGINAL SERIES
HARVEY RICHARDS ASSISTANT EDITOR-ORIGINAL SERIES
IAN SATTLER DIRECTOR EDITORIAL, SPECIAL PROJECTS
AND ARCHIVAL EDITIONS
ANTON KAWASAKI EDITOR
ROBBIN BROSTERMAN DESIGN DIRECTOR-BOOKS
EDDIE BERGANZA EXECUTIVE EDITOR
BOB HARRAS VP - EDITOR IN CHIEF

DC COMICS
DIANE NELSON PRESIDENT
DAN DIDIO AND **JIM LEE** CO-PUBLISHERS
GEOFF JOHNS CHIEF CREATIVE OFFICER
JOHN ROOD EVP - SALES, MARKETING AND BUSINESS DEVELOPMENT
AMY GENKINS SENIOR VP - BUSINESS AND LEGAL AFFAIRS
NAIRI GARDINER SENIOR VP - FINANCE
JEFF BOISON VP - PUBLISHING OPERATIONS
MARK CHIARELLO VP - ART DIRECTION AND DESIGN
JOHN CUNNINGHAM VP - MARKETING
TERRI CUNNINGHAM VP - TALENT RELATIONS AND SERVICES
ALISON GILL SENIOR VP - MANUFACTURING AND OPERATIONS
DAVID HYDE VP - PUBLICITY
HANK KANALZ SENIOR VP - DIGITAL
JAY KOGAN VP - BUSINESS AND LEGAL AFFAIRS, PUBLISHING
JACK MAHAN VP - BUSINESS AFFAIRS, TALENT
NICK NAPOLITANO VP - MANUFACTURING ADMINISTRATION
RON PERAZZA VP - ONLINE
SUE POHJA VP - BOOK SALES
COURTNEY SIMMONS SENIOR VP - PUBLICITY
BOB WAYNE SENIOR VP - SALES

Cover by J.H. Williams III
Publication design by Robbie Biederman

BATWOMAN: ELEGY

Published by DC Comics. Cover, introduction and compilation
Copyright © 2010 DC Comics. All Rights Reserved.

Originally published in single magazine form in DETECTIVE COMICS
#854-860. Copyright © 2009, 2010 DC Comics. All Rights Reserved.
All characters, their distinctive likenesses and related elements
featured in this publication are trademarks of DC Comics.
The stories, characters and incidents featured in this
publication are entirely fictional. DC Comics does not
read or accept unsolicited submissions of ideas, stories
or artwork.

DC Comics, 1700 Broadway, New York, NY 10019
A Warner Bros. Entertainment Company
Printed by Quad/Graphics, Dubuque, IA, USA. 5/06/11.
First Printing. ISBN: 978-1-4012-8146-0

Introduction

BY RACHEL MADDOW

I confess to once giving a copy of Greg Rucka's *Queen and Country: Operation Broken Ground* to a member of the Senate Intelligence Committee, because I thought it might be helpful to the Senator. It's not as crazy as it sounds: get to know Rucka's character Tara Chase and then Google the real modern American spook Dusty Foggo, and see which one you find more edifying.

In Batwoman, Katherine Rebecca Kane is another character written by Rucka that you can't quite believe doesn't exist in the real world. Her recitation of West Point's honor code — "A cadet shall not lie, cheat or steal, nor suffer others to do so" — rings in my ears like Lieutenant Dan Choi reciting the same code to me on television in March 2009, proving that the "Don't Ask, Don't Tell" policy forced him to lie as a condition of his military service.

In Kate Kane's quiet but life-defining drive to serve, there's the veterans of my generation who in the absence of a draft but through nine straight years of war, have done three, four, five combat tours, to come home to a nation that doesn't always quite remember we're at war.

"When you act wrongly, you have to answer for it. Without hiding, without complaint.... That's integrity, and it is the foundation of honor." That's the moral spine on which Kate Kane's battered frame is hung. She is brave and surly and hurt and strong and always on the Batman rule. For all the brilliant literary allusion, mystery, and trademark Rucka attention to detail, what you won't be able to shake when you're done here is that damn compelling lead character.

Well, maybe that and the art.

In a single, wordless panel showing Kate's father's reaction after she tells him why she's been separated from the Army, artist J.H. Williams III captures both a turning point between characters, and a nation's point of decision. It actually feels, right now, in America, the way Colonel Kane looks in that panel, hurt by the plain open ask of his daughter's green eyes.

Yes, cyanogen chloride is a real thing. No, "Southern Misunderstandistan" is not a real place, but you can bet I'll steal it for commenting on our wars, if I haven't done so already by the time you read this. Yes, some of the baddies in the true religion of crime are super genderqueer and yes, guns mix with magic. Get over it. It's all true, it's all gutwrenching, and you love it.

I won't lie to you: I would read anything Greg Rucka wrote. I would read Greg Rucka's grocery lists. I would read Greg Rucka's discarded edits. I would read a Greg Rucka forty-volume soft-hearted navel-gazer about characters I couldn't care less about, if he was capable of writing such a thing, and if he did I'd probably read it out loud to my friends and exclaim and swear about how he made me care.

Batwoman's in good hands here. You'll see.

Rachel Maddow
March, 2010

Rachel Maddow is a political commentator and television host. She has been the anchorwoman of several syndicated talk radio programs and is currently the host of the nightly television program The Rachel Maddow Show on MSNBC.

There was a year, not so very long past, where the world turned without the eyes of its three greatest heroes looking upon it, when Batman, Superman, and Wonder Woman stepped back from their roles.

It was in Gotham City, then, that the symbol of the red bat was first truly noted, though some have speculated that both it and its wearer had been there for quite some time already, watching and waiting. But it was not until the Dark Knight's absence that this new presence became truly known.

This new hero was, in many ways, a reflection of the Batman — the same ruthless pursuit of justice; the same savage need to defend the innocent. But this was not some Robin all-grown-up, nor was it some boy raised to fit boots he had no hope of being able to fill.

This was a woman, the Batwoman, and while there was, indeed, a reflection, it was clear to all who saw her that this was something different. This was not another devotee of the Dark Knight. This woman went her own way.

At the end of this year, the Batwoman fell, captured by a cult devoted to evil, a cult that saw in her the fulfillment of its dark destiny. It was the hand of the cult's leader, the High Madame of the Religion of Crime, that drove a knife into the heart of Batwoman.

She should have died. She nearly did. Instead, it was the High Madame who fell, and the Batwoman who survived. But a wound to the heart is not one easily healed.

It has been a long road back, and now the Batwoman hears whispers in the night: a new High Madame is coming to Gotham.

The Batwoman is looking forward to meeting her....

GREG RUCKA
WRITER

ARTIST
J H WILLIAMS III

DAVE STEWART: colors

ONE **AGITATO**

TODD KLEIN: letters

What a curious feeling!

WRITER
GREG RUCKA

I'm going to >kaf< tell you all your >hkk< faults.

J H WILLIAMS III
ARTIST

SAVE YOUR BREATH...

ELEGY PART 2

DAVE STEWART:
colors

You...

...sha'n't be *beheaded*...

grrrRRRRWWLLl

...NOT THAT I DON'T **APPROVE,** IT'S YOUR LIFE, OF COURSE.

I JUST DON'T THINK IT'S **APPROPRIATE** FOR A **FORMAL** EVENT. IT'S LIKE YOU'RE TRYING TO DRAW **ATTENTION** TO YOURSELF.

NO, JUST MAKING SURE I DON'T STAY **HIDDEN.**

de-doo! de-doo! de-doo!

I THINK SHE LOOKS **GREAT.**

YOU'RE LOOKING VERY NICE YOURSELF, BETTE.

KANE, GO.

SO, COUSIN... HAVEN'T SEEN YOU **AROUND** SINCE I GOT TO TOWN.

I'VE BEEN **BUSY.** YOU STAYING LONG?

ACTUALLY, YEAH, I'M EN-ROLLING AT **GU.**

THAT WAS THE *BASE*, I'VE GOT TO GO.

THE ARMY'S *TIMING*, AS ALWAYS, IS *IMPECCABLE*.

IT'S CALLED *DUTY* FOR A *REASON*, CATHERINE.

SO NOW THAT I'M GOING TO BE LIVING HERE, I WAS THINKING MAYBE WE COULD HANG OUT OR SOMETHING.

IT'S BEEN KIND OF--

EXCUSE ME, I'LL BE RIGHT BACK.

--LONELY...

LIKE FATHER, LIKE DAUGHTER.

IF I **DID** WOULD THAT **STOP** YOU?

I'D LET THE **LADY** DECIDE FOR HERSELF.

YOU GET **ONE** DANCE.

MORE THAN FAIR.

VIRTUS

YOU CAN RELAX, TWICE-NAMED. I'M NOT HERE TO REVEAL YOUR **SECRETS.**

GIVE ME ONE **REASON** I SHOULD **BELIEVE** YOU, ABBOT.

I SAVED YOUR **LIFE** LAST NIGHT. I'D THINK THAT'D BUY ME A **LITTLE** OF YOUR **TRUST.**

IT'S THE **ONLY** REASON I HAVEN'T TURNED YOU **FALSETTO.**

YOU THINK I STILL FOLLOW THE DARK FAITH? THAT I FOLLOW ALICE?

I'M TOLD YOU'RE A **TRUE** BELIEVER.

I **AM.** AND THAT'S MADE ME A **HERETIC.**

THE CRIME BIBLE FORETOLD THE **DEATH** OF THE TWICE-NAMED DAUGHTER OF CAIN.

THE **PROPHECY** SAID BATWOMAN HAD TO **DIE** FOR THE NEW WORLD TO RISE, IT GAVE THE **TIME** AND **PLACE...**

...YET HERE YOU **ARE.** SO THE PROPHECY WAS **WRONG.**

WHICH MEANS YOU'RE SUPPOSED TO **LIVE.**

THAT'S WHY YOU **SAVED** ME?

DAVE STEWART
colors

COLONEL! DAD!

DADDY!

SHE HAS HIM. ALICE HAS MY FATHER.

THERE'S *TWO* REASONS FOR ALICE TO NICK YOUR *OLD MAN,* MISS KANE. FIRST, *BECAUSE* HE'S YOUR OLD MAN...

...AND SECOND, BECAUSE HE'S A *FULL-BIRD* IN THE *ARMY,* WITH *ALL* THE ACCESS THAT GRANTS HIM.

"MOP FOR CW."

GOD HELP ME, ABBOT, I KNOW WHAT ALICE IS *PLANNING.*

WE NEED TO GO TO MY PLACE *FIRST,* THEN THE BASE.

KATE? EVERYTHING *COOL?*

NO.

TODD KLEIN
letters

End of
ELEGY

TWENTY YEARS AGO

YOU THINK DAD'S BACK?

YOU KNOW WHAT HAPPENS IF HE IS. MOM SENDS US TO BED *EARLY* SO THEY CAN HAVE--

...*QUALITY* TIME EWWWWW!

GREG RUCKA
WRITER

DAVE STEWART
COLORS

J.H. WILLIAMS III
ARTIST

TODD KLEIN
LETTERS

...YOUR HOMEWORK AFTER *GYMNASTICS*...

GO 1

...AND I WANT YOU *EACH* TO DO YOUR *OWN* ASSIGNMENTS, OR ELSE I'LL HAVE TO *SEPARATE* YOU.

MOM, NO *FAIR*-- --WE WORK *FASTER* WHEN WE WORK *TOGETHER*!

FASTER, HMM?

SO THAT'S WHY KATE'S BEEN PRETENDING TO BE *YOU* FOR MR. DOUGHERTY'S CLASS, BETH?

NOT *MY* FAULT HE CAN'T TELL US *APART*.

OR *MINE*.

THICK AS *THIEVES*, YOU TWO, AND AS *BAD* AS A PAIR OF THEM.

EXCEPT YOU *FORGET*, I'M YOUR *MOTHER* AND I KNOW *ALL* OF YOUR *TRICKS*.

IT *STOPS* NOW, AND TOMORROW, YOU *BOTH* WILL TELL MR. DOUGHERTY WHAT YOU DID, AND *APOLOGIZE* FOR IT.

MOM! WE'RE GONNA GET IN--

--SO MUCH *TROUBLE*, HE'S GONNA BE--

--SO MAD!

YES, HE IS.

SOMETHING YOU *BOTH* SHOULD HAVE CONSIDERED BEFORE YOU TOOK *ADVANTAGE* OF HIM.

BE CAREFUL WITH THAT ONE, THAT'S THE CHINA--

--GIRLS, HOW WAS SCHOOL? WE NEED TO TALK--

I HATE YOU!

I DON'T WANT TO MOVE TO NATO.

BRUSSELS.

YOU KNOW WHAT I MEAN! YOU ALWAYS KNOW WHAT I MEAN, BETH!

AND I HATE DAD!

KATE!

I DON'T WANT TO MOVE AGAIN! I DON'T WANT TO LIVE IN BELGIUM!

I DON'T WANT TO LEAVE!

BUT YOU DON'T EVEN LIKE LARRY QUINONES.

IT'S NOT FUNNY! ALL OUR FRIENDS ARE HERE!

I DON'T WANT TO LEAVE.

WE'VE GOT EACH OTHER, KATE. WE'LL STILL BE TOGETHER.

WE'LL ALWAYS BE TOGETHER...

SEVEN YEARS AGO

KATE?

KANE, K./B2

WHAT'RE YOU STILL DOING HERE? I THOUGHT YOU WERE LEAVING RIGHT AFTER THE *BANQUET*.

DECIDED I WANTED TO STAY ON *POST*.

CANDY, IT'S RING WEEKEND!

AT LEAST GET A PASS, TAKE YOUR NEW *GLS* OUT FOR A *SPIN*.

RIGHT, BECAUSE THAT'S *SO* WHAT I'D DO.

I'VE GOT BRIGADE WORK, ANYWAY.

YOUR *DAD* DIDN'T COME UP?

THE LTC'S NEW *FIANCÉE* HAD OTHER IDEAS.

HUAH.

HUAH.

KANE

BEING ALONE'S NO GOOD, CANDY.

IT'S OKAY, SOPHIE. I'LL BE ALL RIGHT.

DUTY, HONOR, AND COUNTRY, RIGHT?

TELL YOUR FOLKS I SAID HI.

KANE

GREG RUCKA
WRITER
DAVE STEWART
COLORS

J.H. WILLIAMS III
ARTIST
TODD KLEIN
LETTERS

SPECIAL THANKS TO 1LT DANIEL CHOI (USMA 2003) FOR HIS GENEROUS ASSISTANCE IN RESEARCH FOR THIS ISSUE

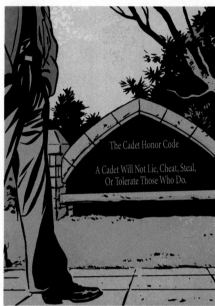

The Cadet Honor Code

A Cadet Will Not Lie, Cheat, Steal, Or Tolerate Those Who Do.

KNEW I'D FIND YOU HERE.

THOUGHT YOU WERE WITH YOUR PARENTS.

AND LEAVE YOU ALONE TO WALLOW IN SELF-PITY?

NO SUCH LUCK, CADET KANE.

CADET KANE REPORTING TO THE BTO AS ORDERED.

COME ON IN, CADET.

YOU CAN STAND AT EASE, KATE.

THANK YOU, SIR.

AN ALLEGATION HAS BEEN BROUGHT TO ME REGARDING YOUR CONDUCT.

SPECIFICALLY, THAT YOU'RE IN VIOLATION OF ARTICLE 125 OF THE UNIFORM CODE OF MILITARY JUSTICE.

I'M OBLIGATED TO INITIATE AN INVESTIGATION INTO *ANY* POTENTIAL VIOLATION OF THE *UCMJ*, AS YOU KNOW.

YES, SIR.

I HAVE SOME *DISCRETION* IN THIS MATTER, HOWEVER.

YOU CAN TELL ME RIGHT NOW THAT THIS IS A *MISTAKE*.

THAT IT'S SOME JOKE, THAT YOU WERE GOOFING AROUND. THAT IT'S A SIMPLE *MISUNDERSTANDING*.

AND THAT IT WILL *NEVER* HAPPEN *AGAIN*.

TELL ME THAT, AND YOU'LL FACE *DISCIPLINARY* ACTION. YOU'LL *LOSE* THE CHANCE TO BE *FIRST CAPTAIN* NEXT SEMESTER.

BUT YOU'LL STILL *GRADUATE,* AND YOU'LL *STAY* IN THE *ARMY*.

I UNDERSTAND, SIR.

I'M DOING THIS BECAUSE YOU'RE A DAMN FINE CADET. BECAUSE I BELIEVE YOU'LL MAKE A DAMN FINE OFFICER.

I'M DOING THIS BECAUSE YOUR *FATHER* IS AS FINE A *SOLDIER* AS I'VE EVER MET, AND FOR THE MEMORY OF YOUR *MOTHER,* ABOUT WHOM I CAN, AND DO, SAY THE *SAME.*

YES, SIR.

MAY I ASK A QUESTION, SIR?

YOU MAY.

THAT'S NOT RELEVANT TO THIS CONVERSATION.

AM I THE *ONLY* CADET FACING THIS ALLEGATION?

I'D LIKE TO KNOW ALL THE SAME, SIR.

AT PRESENT, YOU ARE THE *ONLY* CADET FACING THIS ALLEGATION, YES.

THANK YOU, SIR.

THINK ABOUT THIS, KATE. THINK ABOUT WHAT YOU STAND TO *LOSE.*

YOU'RE AT THE *TOP* OF YOUR CLASS, YOU'RE THE BRIGADE *XO.* DO YOU *REALLY* WANT TO RISK *SEPARATION?* DO YOU REALLY WANT TO RISK A *DISCHARGE?*

SIR, ALL I'VE *EVER WANTED* SINCE MY MOTHER AND SISTER WERE MURDERED IS TO *SERVE.*

HEY, POP.

KATE? THIS IS A SURPRISE.

SHOULDN'T YOU BE ATTENDING CLASS? ARE YOU ON A PASS?

NO, SIR.

I'VE BEEN SEPARATED FROM THE ARMY.

WHAT? WHAT HAPPENED?

COLONEL REYES INFORMED ME I WAS UNDER INVESTIGATION FOR VIOLATING ARTICLE 125.

I COULDN'T SAY WHAT HE NEEDED TO *HEAR.*

ARTICLE 125, THAT'S HOMOSEXUAL CONDUCT.

YES, SIR.

WHY COULDN'T YOU TELL HIM WHAT HE NEEDED TO HEAR?

I'D HAVE BEEN *LYING.*

THEN YOU KEPT YOUR *HONOR* AND YOUR *INTEGRITY.* I'M *PROUD* OF YOU.

YOUR MOTHER WOULD'VE BEEN, TOO.

BUT I'VE GOT TO ASK YOU, KATE...

"...WHAT ARE YOU GOING TO DO NOW?"

"I DON'T KNOW, POP..."

"...I WANTED TO SERVE..."

...YES, I KNOW, IT'S *POSTED*, IT'S THIRTY-FIVE. I WAS DOING ALL OF, LIKE, *FORTY.* YOU TRYING TO MAKE YOUR *QUOTA?*

I CLOCKED YOU DOING FIFTY-TWO, MA'AM. LICENSE AND REGISTRATION, PLEASE.

NO I WASN'T, I WAS *NOT,* I WAS DOING *FORTY,* TOPS.

UH-HUH. HAVE YOU BEEN DRINKING THIS EVENING, MISS, UH, KANE?

WHY? YOU OFFERING TO *BUY* ME ONE?

NO, MA'AM, I...

"...THAT WAS *ALL* I WANTED...

"...NOW THAT'S *GONE*...

"...I'VE GOT *NOTHING*..."

...I'M... JUST...

...MAYBE SOME OTHER TIME.

WHEN?

SORRY?

SOME OTHER TIME *WHEN*, OFFICER...?

...MONTOYA. RENEE MONTOYA.

RENEE MONTOYA.

I'M KATE.

YEAH, I KNOW...

FOUR YEARS AGO

...IT GETS INTO *EVERYTHING*, YOUR *HAIR*, YOUR SOCKS, YOU *NAME* IT.

YOU'RE GONNA HAVE TO *LAUNDER* THE HELL OUT OF THOSE CLOTHES.

NICE JOB HIDING YOUR LITTLE OPERATIONAL *"HEART"* HERE.

BUT ALL THIS STUFF...THIS IS *BEYOND* MIDNIGHT REQUISITION, KATHERINE.

THIS IS *THEFT*.

HELL, ASIDE FROM THE SMOKE AND *CS*, YOU'VE GOT JUST ABOUT EVERY *NON-LETHAL* WE STOCK ON-*BASE* IN HERE.

AND DO *NOT* GET ME *STARTED* ON THE *ELECTRONICS* YOU'VE STOLEN.

I WAS ACTUALLY *RELIEVED* WHEN I REALIZED WHAT YOU WERE DOING WITH ALL THIS STUFF.

BUT HERE'S A LITTLE *BISCUIT* FOR YOU TO CHEW ON, KATE. YOU'RE *NOT* A SOLDIER ANYMORE, AND YOU'RE NOT A COP.

JUST BECAUSE YOU SURVIVED *BEAST* AT THE POINT AND YOU WERE SENIOR ELITE IN *GYMNASTICS* DOESN'T MEAN YOU'RE A DAMN *CRIMEFIGHTER*.

AND IT'S GOING TO *STOP* NOW.

Gun Running

JACKSON   DUNNE

CARTEL?

BIKER GANGS?

TERRORISM?

NO.

HOOAH.

...BUT NOT LIKE *THIS*...

...IF YOU'RE *GOING* TO DO IT, YOU NEED TO DO IT *RIGHT*, KATE, YOU NEED TO GET SQUARED AWAY...

...WE'RE TALKING ABOUT THE RAZOR'S EDGE STUFF, THAT'S TWO, MAYBE THREE YEARS OF *ADVANCED* TRAINING...

...I'M THINKING...THERE'S A GUY I KNOW, EX-S.A.S., MAYBE I CAN REACH OUT TO HIM. A COUPLE *OTHERS* WHO OWE ME FAVORS.

SOME OF THE *URBAN* AND *NON-LETHAL* SPECIALISTS, MAYBE GET YOU AND FOSTER TOGETHER. HE'S STILL IN *INTEL*, USED TO WORK WITH YOUR MOTHER.

AND THERE'S NO WAY YOU CAN KEEP DOING THIS *ALONE*.

WE'RE IN THIS *TOGETHER*.

I LOVE YOU, POP.

YEAH?

JUST WAIT UNTIL YOU SEE WHAT I DO TO *THIS* PLACE.

"MAKE NO MISTAKE: YOU DO THIS, YOU'RE GOING TO *WAR*.

"DEFINE THE *GOAL*. DEFINE THE *OBJECTIVE*. DEFINE THE *TERMS* OF *VICTORY*.

"BECAUSE IF VICTORY MEANS BRINGING YOUR MOTHER AND SISTER BACK, YOU'VE *ALREADY* LOST.

"...TO KEEP *ONE* PERSON FROM HAVING THEIR LIFE *SHATTERED* IN VIOLENCE...

"...AND TO COME HOME *ALIVE* WHEN YOU'RE DONE...

--NO, NO, NO, **NO,** I TOLD YOU, **BELUGA...**

...THE SENATOR **HATES** SEVRUGA. GIVES HIM A **HEADACHE.**

AND TELL GINNY THAT THERE'S A **FRACTURE** IN THE ICE SCULPTURE. I WANT A **REPLACEMENT** BY FOUR.

HELLO, CATHERINE.

KATE?

KATIE! WHEN DID YOU GET **BACK?**

LAST YOUR FATHER SAID, YOU WERE IN MALAYSIA OR INDONESIA OR SOMEPLACE TERRIBLY **HOT** AND **HUMID!**

WE DIDN'T THINK WE'D SEE YOU UNTIL THE HIGH HOLY DAYS--

--LOOK AT YOU! YOU LOOK **TERRIFIC!** DID YOU LOSE **WEIGHT?**

I GUESS--

MAKES ME WISH THAT **I** COULD SPEND TWO YEARS TROTTING AROUND THE **GLOBE** ON SOMEONE ELSE'S **MONEY!**

DOES YOUR FATHER KNOW YOU'RE **BACK?** HOLD ON--

--JAKE! **JAKE!** COME HERE!

Detective Comics
VARIANT COVER GALLERY

Bonus Material

BY J.H. WILLIAMS III & GREG RUCKA

KATHY KANE - CHARACTER SHEET - ROUGHS
A COMPLETELY DIFFERENT LOOK THAN PREVIOUSLY
MORE DEFINITIVE PERSONALITY - RETRO - ROCKABILLY LOOK
SHE IS REALLY INTO ALTERNATIVE AND EDGY MUSIC -
    A BIT OF ● PUNK - PSYCHOBILLY - GOTH AND REFLECTS THIS IN HER
    PERSONAL STYLE - THIS LOOK HERE IS JUST ONE ASPECT

HER SKIN IS LITERALLY
VAMPIRE WHITE PORCELAIN
VERY LITTLE COLOR AT
    ALL

BLUE BIRD
TATTOO

EYES ARE GREEN
AND SHE WEARS DARK
    RED LIPSTICK
COOL TONED EYE
SHADOW

LARGE
NAUTICAL STAR
TATTOO

WHITE BOW

Jim – This is the mirror spread.

ONE:
Full body shot, BATWOMAN. Iconic. More an art element, as discussed, than an actual storytelling panel. This is the mirror to Panel Eight.

NO COPY.

TWO:
Interior of the MAIN COMPARTMENT, as BATWOMAN enters.

ALICE is standing at the PUMP CONTROLS, and she's livid. The fucking thing's broken! This isn't fair! Nothing's fair!! Maybe she's holding one of the BROKEN WHEELS in one hand.

In her OTHER HAND, she's holding a PISTOL, pointed at BATWOMAN.

1 BATWOMAN:	You're done, High Madame.
2 BATWOMAN:	I **disabled** the pump, you're not killing **anyone** today.
3 ALICE:	I ca'n't **stand** this any **longer**!

THREE:
BATWOMAN shielding herself with her CAPE – covering her head with it – as ALICE empties the GUN at her. The BARRAGE of shots is knocking BATWOMAN to a knee.

ALICE is screaming at BATWOMAN as she fires.

4 ALICE:	And as for you!
5 ALICE:	As for you, I'll shake you into a kitten, that I will!!!
6 SFX:	BLAMMBLAMMBLAMMBLAMMBLAMMBLAMMklk
klkklk	

FOUR:
BATWOMAN, on one knee, lowering the CAPE to look.

ALICE has dropped the gun, already going out the ROOF HATCH. Maybe just her legs visible as she climbs out.

| 7 BATWOMAN: | Dammit, **stop**! |

[continued]

FIVE:

Exterior of the plane, ALICE is pulling herself along the wing on hands and knees to reach one of the CANISTERS, determined to succeed. The WIND whips her hair and clothes violently.

BATWOMAN is just emerging from the HATCH behind her, shouting at her. Her GRAPPLING GUN is in her hand.

8 BATWOMAN: It's **over**, Alice!

SIX:

BATWOMAN fires the GRAPPLING GUN, the line catching ALICE around one ANKLE.

ALICE has grabbed the CANNISTER RIG with one hand, holding on to it, and with the other is pointing her REMAINING PISTOL back at BATWOMAN.

She's crying uncontrollably. She doesn't want to lose. She can't lose. If she loses, who is she?

9 SFX: paff

10 ALICE: The **face** is what one **goes** by, generally.

SEVEN:

ALICE SHOOTS, hitting the GRAPPLING GUN in BATWOMAN'S HAND

BATWOMAN is losing the GRAPPLING GUN, obviously.

11 SFX: BLAMMM

12 BATWOMAN: ahg!

13 ALICE: Who am **I**, then?

EIGHT:

Full body shot, ALICE, iconic, the mirror image of Panel One.

NO COPY.

ONE:

Wash in on the SYMBOL of the Kane Heresy, the Dark Faith's circle emblem, with a CHALICE on its side, spilling WINE or BLOOD.

We *may* be able to see the top of ABBOT'S HEAD in this panel.

For the record, the Heresy is based in the ruins of pre-No Man's Land Gotham, in what was once a small church before the earthquake. The location serves as a combination place of worship, as well as a dormitory/home for those members of the Heresy unable to control their change, ie, those Monster Men who can't, for whatever reason, revert their forms to "human."

They try to keep it nice, here, but let's face it – it's an old church that was damaged in an earthquake and is buried under ground. How nice can that be? Thing to remember is that Alice's Dark Faith has bucks; Abbot's has nada.

1 ABBOT:	My story. Listen, because it is yours, too.
2 ABBOVE:	The prophesy is told in The Blasphemies, in the Book of Lilith.
3 ABBOT:	That on the eighteenth day past the feast of All Saints…

TWO:

Angle, past Doctor MALLORY KIMBALL, as she enters her office at St. Luke's Hospital, in Gotham.

MALLORY has stopped short, reacting to BATWOMAN standing in her office.

Jim, I'd like to play this differently than in a Batman title, if that makes sense – in a Batman book, Mallory would enter the office, and then we'd see Batman come out of the shadows behind her or something like that. I don't want to do that here with Kate; it's against her character, and frankly we've seen it a million times before.

With that in mind, yes, Batwoman has been waiting for Mallory, but she's not trying to scare her or ninja-tactics her. Not sure where this should put her in the room, or what pose she should be in, but she's been waiting.

BATWOMAN still has the injuries she was carrying last issue – the conceit is that all of the "present" stuff is taking place the same night, which is also the same night as the events of issues 3 and 4.

This means BATWOMAN may still be bleeding from one or two of her various wounds – that stab wound that Alice gave her in the arm is particularly nasty.

4 BATWOMAN:	Doctor Kimball.
5 BATWOMAN:	I need a **favor**.

THREE:

Back to ABBOT, panning down a bit, maybe swinging around to look at him, as if he's speaking directly to us. He's wearing his human form.

6 ABBOT:	…the Apostle of the First would come to Gotham…
7 ABBOT:	…and there he would murder the "Twice-Named Daughter of Cain."

FOUR:
BATWOMAN is holding out the TWO SAMPLE TUBES from last issue, offering them to MAL-LORY. BATWOMAN is doing this with her wounded arm.

MALLORY is reacting to the sight of the STAB WOUND on Batwoman.

8 BATWOMAN:	I need a DNA test run on these samples.
9 BATWOMAN:	I need to confirm they're from **monozygotic** twins.
10 MALLORY:	You're **wounded**.
11 BATWOMAN:	Will you do this for me?

FIVE:
On ABBOT. He's beginning to transform into his WOLFMAN form.

12 ABBOT:	So many times, the High Madame poured these words in my ear.
13 ABBOT:	So many times, it had to be the **truth**.

SIX:
MALLORY has taken the samples in one hand, already setting them aside. With her other hand, she's taken BATWOMAN'S wounded arm by the WRIST. Mallory is clearly concerned about the wound.

BATWOMAN is still in the same place she was last issue, and she's barely feeling the injury, now. Focused entirely on Mallory – the injury doesn't matter, what matters is the DNA test, that's the only thing she cares about right now.

14 MALLORY:	You've been **stabbed**—
15 BATWOMAN:	Doctor Kimball. Mallory. Will you test them for me?
16 MALLORY:	I can have the results by tomorrow night. Now take off your gauntlet, let me take a look at—

SEVEN:
On ABBOT, and he's fully transformed now. Growling out his words.

17 ABBOT:	It rrrr had to be grrr **truth**.

EIGHT:
MALLORY reacting.

BATWOMAN has pulled her hand back, already turning, heading to the window. Business here is done, time to go.

18 BATWOMAN:	I'll be back tomorrow night.

NINE:
Tight on ABBOT, his WEREWOLF EYES.

19 ABBOT:	It rrrr **wasn't**.

GREG RUCKA

is a thriller novelist who became one of the premier writers for
DC Comics in the last decade. His work on BATMAN brought fresh attention
to the character and the inhabitants of Gotham City. Additionally, he won the
Eisner award for best story with GOTHAM CENTRAL's "Half a Life." His other DC credits
include ADVENTURES OF SUPERMAN, CHECKMATE, DETECTIVE COMICS, WONDER WOMAN,
ACTION COMICS and 52. Rucka is married to fellow writer Jen Van Meter and they make
their home in Portland, Oregon.

J.H. WILLIAMS III

entered the comics field in 1991 and immediately began getting attention for his finely crafted
work on such titles as BATMAN, STARMAN and his co-creation (with D. Curtis Johnson), CHASE.
His acclaimed artistry was later seen on SON OF SUPERMAN, SEVEN SOLIDERS OF VICTORY and
JONAH HEX, and he has received multiple Eisner nominations for his work on co-creations
DESOLATION JONES (with Warren Ellis), and PROMETHEA (with Alan Moore).
Williams and his wife, Wendy, live in California.

DAVE STEWART

began his career as an intern at Dark Horse Comics, and then quickly moved into
coloring comics. His impressive credits include DC: THE NEW FRONTIER, HUMAN TARGET,
SUPERMAN/BATMAN, CATWOMAN: WHEN IN ROME, *Captain America*, *Daredevil*,
Joss Whedon's *Fray*, Mike Mignola's *Hellboy: The Third Wish* and *B.P.R.D.*, Gerard Way's
The Umbrella Academy, and Michael Chabon's *The Amazing Adventures of The Escapist*.
He has won several Eisner Awards for his coloring work, and also colored
Tim Sale's art from the TV series *Heroes*.